6639

for
Charles

Poor Richard in France

by

F. N. MONJO

pictures by
BRINTON TURKLE

HOLT, RINEHART AND WINSTON
New York, Chicago, San Francisco

Library of Congress Cataloging in Publication Data

Monjo, F   N
   Poor Richard in France.

   SUMMARY: Benjamin Franklin's seven-year-old grandson recounts the events of his grandfather's visit to France seeking aid for the revolutionaries in America.

   1. Franklin, Benjamin, 1706–1790—Juvenile fiction. [1. Franklin, Benjamin, 1706–1790—Fiction] I. Turkle, Brinton, illus. II. Title.
PZ7.M75Po   [E]   72-76582
ISBN 0-03-088597-3 (Holt Reinforced ed.)

A HOLT REINFORCED EDITION

Text copyright © 1973 by Ferdinand Monjo and
Louise L. Monjo
Illustrations copyright © 1973 by Brinton Turkle

Published simultaneously in Canada by
Holt, Rinehart and Winston of Canada, Limited.
ISBN 0-03-088598-1
Library of Congress Catalog Card Number 72-76582
Printed in the United States of America

Type design by Aileen Friedman

Published, October, 1973
Third Printing, May, 1975

CONTENTS

CHAPTER ONE

On Board the "Reprisal"
December 1776

Grandfather and I are playing chess
in his cabin.
There's nothing Grandfather loves better
than playing chess.
I usually lose.
We're sailing to France.
We left Philadelphia
more than a month ago.
My cousin, Temple, is with us, too.
But today Temple's seasick.
When we get to Paris,
Temple's going to be Grandfather's secretary.

"Open both those cabin windows wide,
Benny," says Grandfather.
"It's time for me to take my air bath!"
Then Grandfather takes off all his clothes.
He breathes the fresh salty air,
and we start playing chess again.
Temple doesn't like it
when Grandfather undresses
for his air bath.
He says Grandfather is too free.
But Grandfather doesn't mind

2

what Temple says.

He takes an air bath every day.

Grandfather's nearly seventy years old.

He's mighty smart.

He taught himself

French,

and Spanish,

and Latin.

I was named after him.

My name is Benjamin Franklin Bache.

I'm seven.

When Grandfather was a boy in Boston,
his father used to say something to him—
it's from the Bible:
"Seest thou a man
diligent in his business?
He shall stand before kings."
And Grandfather *was* diligent
in his business.
When he first came to Philadelphia,
all the money he had was
one Dutch dollar and a copper shilling.
But he became a printer.
He used to print
a book for farmers.
It was called
Poor Richard's Almanack.
Grandfather wrote things in it,
mostly telling folks what to do
if they wanted to stop being poor
and get rich.
Here are some of the things Grandfather wrote:

"Honesty is the best policy."

"A penny saved is a penny earned."

"The rotten apple spoils his companions."

"The sleeping fox catches no poultry."

Well, Grandfather got to be
the richest printer in Philadelphia.
And then he went to Europe.
And—just as the Bible said—
when he got there,
he stood before kings!
Grandfather's already met
four kings in Europe.
And if everything goes all right
when we get to France,
he may even meet his fifth king—
that's the king of France, Louis XVI.

"I think that's enough fresh air,
for one morning, Benny," says Grandfather.
"Fetch me something to put on."
I go and fetch Grandfather
an old blue velvet coat.
"No, no, Benny," says Grandfather.
"Not *that* one. I'm saving it for later."
"Why's that, Grandfather?" says I.

So Grandfather tells me.
"I wore that blue coat
several years ago in London,
Benny, just before the war
broke out," says Grandfather.
"It was the day I begged
those stubborn Englishmen
not to send their soldiers to Boston.
I warned their stubborn,
foolish king . . ."
"George III?" says I.
Grandfather nods.
"I warned His Majesty
that it would come to war.
But his men called me
a fool, and a thief, and a liar,
until I decided it was no use,
and that I'd best sail home again."
"And it was this blue coat
you wore that day?" says I.
"Indeed it was," laughs Grandfather.

King George III

"So we'll just tuck it away and save it
until we win this war.
Then, Benny, I'll wear it again."
I don't know what Grandfather means.
I don't think he'll wear it again
in a hurry.
We're losing the war, it seems to me.

There are British soldiers
in New York City.
Mother and Father and my little brother
are home, safe, in Philadelphia.
But who knows for how long?
My Uncle Will, Temple's father,
is in jail. He's a Tory.
A Tory is somebody
who sides with the British,
instead of with General Washington.
Uncle Will won't fight
against King George III.
That's why he's in jail.
Grandfather felt terrible
about Uncle Will.
Temple did, too.
Grandfather says that's what
war does to families.
Splits them apart, sometimes.
He hates war.

"I never saw a good war
or a bad peace," says Grandfather.
"But, if you decide
to give a man a blow at all, Benny,
make sure you give him a *douser!*"
(Temple says a douser
is a real hard clout).

Temple says we're sailing to France
to get some help for the United States.
Grandfather says this little sloop
we're on, the *Reprisal*,
just might be captured by the British
before we ever get there.
Temple says that if the British
catch us, they might try to
hang Grandfather!
Because Grandfather's a rebel!
And so's Temple.
And so am I.

This morning the captain took
Grandfather and me
all over the ship.
Grandfather walks sort of slow,
because he has the gout.
That's a disease
that makes your toes ache.
There's a load of indigo in the hold.
Indigo is a plant they use
in making a deep blue dye.
Grandfather's going to sell the indigo
when we get to Paris.
Indigo smells *terrible!*
Ugh!

People call Grandfather "Doctor" Franklin.
Do you want to know why?
Because Grandfather's a scientist.
He found out that lightning
and electricity
are the same thing.
And he put the first lightning rods
on buildings, too.
Grandfather says
lightning rods work best if
they're pointed on top.
Then, in a thunderstorm,

the lightning strikes the point
and runs down the rod into the ground,
and the building won't catch fire.

Temple says
when King George III
put lightning rods on his palace,
he wouldn't let the tops be pointed.
King George made the workmen
put big round *knobs* on top of the rods!

Grandfather laughed when they
told him about it.
"How like His Majesty," said Grandfather,
"to prefer the blunt to the sharp!"
(I suppose Grandfather thinks
King George is kind of stupid.)

Grandfather hates sea voyages in winter.
And he's sick of eating salt beef.
And now it's December,
so we should be in France
in a few days.

CHAPTER TWO

The Face of the Man in the Moon
December 1776

The British missed their chance
to hang Grandfather.
We landed safely in France yesterday.
Temple is feeling better,
now that we're on land.

Our trip is supposed to be secret.
But everybody in France
seems to know who Grandfather is.
And they all want to meet him.
Here's what they call Grandfather:
"Le grand Docteur Franklin!"

(Temple says that means
"the great Dr. Franklin.")
And here's what they holler
whenever they see him:
"Vive le Bonhomme Richard!"
(Temple says *that* means
"Long live Poor Richard!").

Grandfather says that
half the people in France
think he's a Quaker,
because he doesn't wear
fancy clothes, or carry a sword.
All the important men here
wear velvet and satin,
and lace and gold braid,
and swords and wigs,
and ruffles and ribbons,
and hats with plumes.
Not Grandfather.
He has no wig.
He wears his plain brown suit,
and his plain linen shirt,
and his spectacles,
and carries his
crab-apple walking stick
instead of a sword.

Grandfather has lived most of his life
in Philadelphia—the biggest city
in America.
But lots of Frenchmen
seem to think that Grandfather
used to live way off on the frontier,
deep in the forest,
like Daniel Boone!
Grandfather told Temple,
"The French would like
to think of me
as the Sage of the Wilderness."
And with that he put on
his fur cap!
That fur cap makes him look
just like Daniel Boone!
And now he wears it everywhere!

It was nearly Christmas
when we got to Paris at last.
Everybody in France has heard
how we Americans are fighting to be
free of King George III.
And most of the people
hope we're going to win!

Temple says there's not much hope
that we can win,
unless we get some help from France.
But if Grandfather can get
the French king to help us,
maybe we can lick that British bulldog!
Grandfather sold the indigo
from the *Reprisal*.
Temple says he'll use that money
to buy guns and cannon
for General Washington's army, back home.

All the ladies in Paris
want to kiss Grandfather.
But Grandfather says it isn't so easy
to kiss French ladies.
Here's why you can't kiss them
on the lips. It's impolite.
And you can't kiss them
on the cheeks, either,
because they wear
big bright circles of rouge there.
That means you have to kiss them
on the neck!
So that's what Grandfather does.

Temple doesn't like
any of this kissing.
He says Grandfather
is *much too free*.
But Temple must be wrong,
because everybody in Paris
is wild about Grandfather.
All the coachmen,
and servants, and scullery maids,
think he has come to France
to make them rich
and to teach them how to be free!

And that's not all.
There are pictures and statues
of Grandfather
for sale all over Paris.
You can buy his face
in marble, or bronze, or plaster.

His face is painted on
watches,
clocks,
vases,
dishes,
snuffboxes,
rings,
handkerchiefs,
and pocketknives.

Temple was shocked
when Grandfather said
he wouldn't be surprised to see
his face, someday, painted on
a *vase de nuit*.
Temple wouldn't tell me
what a *vase de nuit* is,
so I had to ask Grandfather.
Grandfather laughed and said,
"A *vase de nuit*, Benny,
is what we call a chamber pot!"

Temple says
Grandfather doesn't take things
seriously enough.
Grandfather says,
"I think this old face of mine
must be better known in France
than the face of the man in the moon!"

CHAPTER THREE

Waiting in Passy
1777

None of the news from home
is very good.
Mother and Father say
that one British army under General Howe
is moving up from the south,
trying to take Philadelphia.
Another army under General Burgoyne
is getting ready to come down from Canada,
and cut off New England from New York.

Grandfather has rented a nice house
in Passy, just outside of Paris.
I go to school in Paris
and come out to Grandfather's,
in Passy, for Saturday and Sunday.

Mother wrote a letter to Grandfather
asking him to send her some
black pins, and lace,
and feathers, from France.
Grandfather wouldn't send her
any of that stuff.
He wrote back:
"Your sending for long black pins,
and lace, and feathers
disgusted me as much as if
you had put salt into my strawberries.
I cannot furnish my children,
in wartime, with foolish modes
and luxuries. If you wear
your cambric ruffles, as I do,
and take care *not* to mend the holes,
they will come, in time, to be lace.
And feathers, my dear girl,
may be had in America,
from every cock's tail."

I'm learning Latin at school.

Here's something that was written

by Monsieur Turgot,

a French friend of Grandfather's.

Here it is:

"Eripuit caelo fulmen sceptrumque tyrannis."

This Latin is all about Grandfather. It says:

"He snatched the lightning bolt from Heaven,

and the scepter from the tyrant."

You know what that means?

It means that it was Grandfather

who found out that lightning

and electricity are the same thing.

And it means that he snatched

some power away from the tyrant—

King George III.

Grandfather did *that* when he helped

write the Declaration of Independence,

and set all of us Americans free,

last year, on the Fourth of July.

Over: Signing the Declaration of Independence

Temple says
Grandfather might have been asked
to write that Declaration
all by himself—
without Thomas Jefferson—
if they hadn't thought Grandfather
would put a *joke* in it somewhere.

Temple says there are lots of spies
in Paris, and in Passy,
trying to find out
what Grandfather's doing here.
But Grandfather says all he wants to do
is make a treaty saying that
France and the United States are friends.

But Grandfather can't do much about
that treaty now, because he can't
get to see the king of France.
The king of France
doesn't want to meet Grandfather yet.

He's waiting to see how
General Washington makes out
with the war.
Grandfather asked the French
to give him some ships
for the American navy.
King Louis said no.
But Grandfather will
keep on trying.

Even so, Grandfather's
doing a lot to help
General Washington.
Sometimes he has to have
secret meetings.
Here's what he does.

Grandfather loves to go swimming.

Even in winter.

He's the strongest swimmer

you ever saw.

If he has a secret message to deliver,

sometimes he swims out

into the middle of the River Seine.

There's a big float

anchored out there.

It has bathhouses on it.

So, the other man swims out

to the bathhouse, too.

And he and Grandfather sit there

and talk until their business is done.

That way, nobody can hear what they're

talking about. Not even Temple.

Temple says Grandfather has arranged
to smuggle guns
and gunpowder and cannon
from France to America.
Temple says King Louis
knows all about it—
though he pretends he doesn't.

Grandfather still has
lots of ladies to kiss here in Passy.
Two of the ladies he likes the most
live nearby.
One is Madame Helvétius.
She's a widow.
She's sort of old, but
she's rich and she's still pretty.
Temple was so upset when
Grandfather asked Madame Helvétius
to marry him!
But Madame Helvétius said no.
She has a little ginger-colored lap dog,
named Poupou.

She's always kissing Poupou.
Sometimes Poupou wets.
When that happens, Madame Helvétius laughs,
and Grandfather laughs, too.

Another lady Grandfather likes a lot
is Madame Brillon.
She's as young and pretty as she can be.
She and Grandfather
play lots of chess together.
One time Grandfather was winning the game.
He took Madame Brillon's king
right off the board!
Madame Brillon said:
"That's against the rules.
You're not allowed to take the king!"
Grandfather laughed and said,
"In America, *we* do!"

Another time, when Grandfather
went to Madame Brillon's house
to play chess,
Madame Brillon was in the bathtub.
Temple scolded Grandfather when
he found out what happened!
Because she and Grandfather
had their game of chess in the bathroom
just the same!

CHAPTER FOUR

The Blue Coats' Revenge
December 1777

The news from home doesn't get any better.
We've heard a rumor that says
General Howe and his British soldiers
have taken Philadelphia.
But we don't know if it's true.
If Howe *has* taken Philadelphia,
Mother and Father will have to run away.
Grandfather laughs and says,
"Howe hasn't taken Philadelphia.
Philadelphia has taken Howe."
(Temple says *that* means
Grandfather hopes Howe will spend
so much time going to parties
in Philadelphia that he'll
forget about fighting the war).

We don't hear anything about
an American victory. And until we do,
France won't sign our treaty.
Temple says Grandfather is
mighty anxious for King Louis to sign it.
But Grandfather doesn't want to let on.
So he pretends everything's perfect.
He goes to plays in Paris.
Other days he goes swimming
in the river.
And he tries to keep King Louis
from knowing how worried he is!

Today, December 4, we got
the best news!
Listen to what happened!
General Burgoyne's whole British army
has surrendered to the Americans!
It all happened back in October,
up near Albany, at Saratoga!

Temple says this is the big victory
Grandfather's been hoping for.
Grandfather says, "Benny, this time
we really gave Burgoyne a douser!
Now maybe King Louis will think
we Yankees can win this war!"

January 1778

I've been too excited to study my Latin,
or anything else at school.
Today, January 8,
Grandfather heard
that France was ready to sign!

February 1778

Today is Friday, February 6.
Grandfather is getting ready
to go to Paris.
He's going to meet King Louis' helpers.

They're all set to sign
the treaty of friendship
between the United States and France.
Temple's going, too.
Just before Grandfather walked out the door,
I said, "Grandfather! You're
wearing your old blue coat!"
"Yes, Benny," says Grandfather,
"the old coat I wore back there in London
the day the British called me those hard names.
But now the tables are turned," he grinned.
"So I'm wearing it,
to give it a little revenge!"

CHAPTER FIVE

A Ship for Poor Richard
June 1778

That's about all there is to the story.
Grandfather signed the treaty.
The French have gone to war with England.
King Louis is sending
armies of soldiers and fleets of ships
to General Washington.
Temple says we're bound to win now!

We met a trim American navy fellow
the other day.
His name is Captain John Paul Jones.
Temple says that Captain Jones asked
Grandfather
to try to get him a good new ship,
and Grandfather said he'd do what he could.
Now that the treaty is signed,
Grandfather smiles more than ever,
even when he has the gout.

Temple says that some more Americans
have come to Passy to help Grandfather:
Mr. John Adams of Massachusetts,
and his wife, Abigail Adams,
and their son, Master Johnny.
Mrs. Adams doesn't
wear a speck of rouge.
Temple says Mrs. Adams doesn't like
the way Madame Helvétius
hugs and kisses Grandfather.
Temple says she doesn't like
Poupou, either.
Temple says Mrs. Adams says
she saw Poupou wet the floor,
and Madame Helvétius wiped it up with her shift.

"What's a shift, Temple?" I said.
Temple wouldn't tell me.
But Grandfather did.
"A shift, Benny," said Grandfather,
"is a lady's petticoat."
Nothing seems to upset Grandfather.
Not even the Adamses.

Grandfather went to the palace
the other day to meet·
King Louis of France.
The king said he would always be
a friend of the United States.
And when Grandfather met
Queen Marie Antoinette,
she stopped playing cards long enough
to talk to him about the war in America.
King Louis gave Grandfather
his picture, set with 280 diamonds!
Temple says they're worth
more than five thousand dollars!

Over: Grandfather at the French court

Grandfather even got a big French warship
for Captain John Paul Jones.
Captain Jones is so grateful to Grandfather
that he's going to name it for *him*.
He's going to call his ship
the *Bonhomme Richard*!

And that's all there is to tell.
Except that *next* year Grandfather says
I'm going to have to go to school
in Switzerland—because they
don't have any kings there.

Grandfather says we aren't going
to have any kings in America, either,
after we win this war!

And you know what Grandfather says
about Captain John Paul Jones?
He says that when he sails out
in his *Bonhomme Richard*,
he'll give the British a douser!

Benjamin Franklin's two grandsons, Benjamin Franklin Bache (seven) and William Temple Franklin (seventeen), did indeed accompany their famous grandfather on his historic mission to Paris in October 1776, while we were fighting the American Revolution. And Captain John Paul Jones sailed to Brest in June 1778, and in February 1779, renamed the decrepit old French *Duras*, forty guns, the *Bonhomme Richard*, in Franklin's honor. On September 23, 1779, he gave the British a "douser," for that day off Scarborough Head was fought his famous victory over the British *Serapis*—the fight in which, when asked if he would strike his colors, Jones replied, "I have not yet begun to fight."

Franklin was adored in France, perhaps even more extravagantly than he was in America, for George Washington was the great hero of the Revolution in this country while Franklin personified—for the French—all their own strivings for freedom, which they saw coming to fulfillment, in America, because of the work of such men as "le Bonhomme Richard."

Franklin's achievement in securing the Treaty of Amity and Commerce with France has been called the greatest feat of diplomacy in American history. It was one of the crowning events of his fifty-year-old career of public service, one of the most memorable acts in his life—but a life which was so rich and varied and many-sided that most of his interests, writings, studies, and inventions could not even be mentioned here in this brief fictional glimpse.

The shrewd old sage remained in France another six years or so, until Cornwallis surrendered at Yorktown, and Franklin and the other American commissioners signed a treaty of peace there with the British, in which the United States was recognized as a sovereign nation.

The last great deed in Franklin's long life (1706–1790) was his service as a delegate from Pennsylvania to the Constitutional Convention in 1787.

William Temple Franklin (1760–1823), who was called "Franklinet" by some of the ladies in France, spent most of the rest of his life in England with his staunchly Loyalist father, William Franklin (1730–1813). He later edited Franklin's papers, and even bowdlerized an edition of his outspoken grandsire's famous *Autobiography*.

Benjamin Franklin Bache (1769–1798) died of yellow fever, at twenty-nine. He had been nicknamed "Lightning-Rod, Junior," and had published a newspaper in Philadelphia, the *Aurora*, which supported Jefferson's party against the Federalists—Washington and Adams.

And in one of the great ironic twists of history, the aid—in fleets and soldiers and money—which King Louis XVI gave to America during her revolution, so increased his country's national debt that the huge French deficit which thus piled up became one of the major reasons for France's plunging into revolution herself in 1789.

But before that happened, Thomas Jefferson went to France in 1784 as our ambassador—for Franklin had asked to be relieved. The French diplomat, Vergennes, asked Jefferson: "You replace Dr. Franklin?" "Ah, no," Jefferson replied, with a shake of his head. "No one can replace him. I am only his successor."

ABOUT THE AUTHOR

While growing up in Stamford, Connecticut, F. N. Monjo acquired a lively sense of history. A descendant of Spanish fur traders, within his own family he heard anecdotes of events going back to Civil War times. "Listening to stories like these brought history alive so vividly for me that I was never able to read it, later, as if it were a mere collection of facts and dates."

A graduate of Columbia University, F. N. Monjo became a book editor specializing in children's literature. ". . . as an editor I began to realize that most of the fun of history lay in the details that most children's books seemed to omit. So I resolved to try writing some books for young children, limited to incidents or mere glimpses from history, but allowing enough leisure and space to be able to include the details that help so much to bring the scene to life."

To date the author has published nine popular books for young readers. He lives in Manhattan with his wife, who is a first-grade teacher, and their four children.

ABOUT THE ARTIST

Brinton Turkle originally trained for the stage at the Carnegie Institute, but then decided to try his hand as an artist. He worked for a time in advertising where he was so successful he decided to make art his career. His book illustrations were especially popular and he began to write, as well as to illustrate, picture books for young readers. In 1970, his book *Thy Friend, Obadiah* was a Caldecott honor book.

ABOUT THE BOOK

The text for *Poor Richard* was set in Janson Linofilm. The preseparated art was prepared in charcoal crayon and pastel chalk by the artist. The book was printed in two colors by offset.